WORDS THEIR WAY®

WORD STUDY IN ACTION • EMERGENT-EARLY LETTER NAME

Glenview, Illinois

Boston, Massachusetts

Chandler, Arizona

Upper Saddle River, New Jersey

ALWAYS LEARNING

PEARSON

Photographs

Every effort has been made to secure permission and provide appropriate credit for photographic material. The publisher deeply regrets any omission and pledges to correct errors called to its attention in subsequent editions.

Unless otherwise acknowledged, all photographs are the property of Pearson Education, Inc.

Photo locators denoted as follows: Top (T), Center (C), Bottom (B), Left (L), Right (R), Background (Bkgd)

Cover (C) Glow Images, (T) Getty Images; **1** (Hat) ©Heath Doman/Shutterstock, (Peach) ©Nikolai Pozdeev/Shutterstock, (Bat) Getty Images, (Cherry) Photos to Go/Photolibrary, (Strawberry) Siri Stafford/Thinkstock, (Mop) Stockbyte/Thinkstock, (Apple) Thinkstock; **3** (Hat) ©Heath Doman/Shutterstock, (Apple) Thinkstock; **4** (Hat) ©Heath Doman/Shutterstock, (Apple) Thinkstock; **5** (Tree) ©Borislav Gnjidic/Shutterstock, (Horse, Fish) ©Eric Isselée/Shutterstock, (Bear) ©Eric Isselée/Shutterstock, (Bird) ©Royalty-Free/Corbis, (Flowers) ©Tony Lilley/Alamy, (Rope) ©Valzan/Shutterstock, (Turtle) Getty Images, (Butterfly) Jupiter Images; **7** (Horse) ©Eric Isselée/Shutterstock, (Rope) ©Valzan/Shutterstock; **8** (Horse) ©Eric Isselée/Shutterstock, (Rope) ©Valzan/Shutterstock; **13** (Corn) Jupiter Images, (Stuffed Animal) Shutterstock, (Jumprope, Apple) Thinkstock; **15** (Cherry) Photos to Go/Photolibrary; **16** (Cherry) Photos to Go/Photolibrary; **17** (Hat) ©Heath Doman/Shutterstock, (Mitt) Jupiter Images; **21** (Pizza) ©Nitr/Shutterstock, (Bread) Hemera Technologies, (Juice, Cherry) Photos to Go/Photolibrary, (Apple) Thinkstock; **23** (Corn) Jupiter Images, (Lemonade) Thinkstock; **24** (Corn) Jupiter Images, (Lemonade) Thinkstock; **25** (Trees) ©Majeczka/Shutterstock, (Bear) ©Eric Isselée/Shutterstock, (Rose) ©Tatiana Popova/Shutterstock, (Bread) Hemera Technologies; **27** (Hair) ©OJO Images Ltd./Alamy; **28** (Hair) ©OJO Images Ltd./Alamy; **29** (Eye) ©Darren Baker/Shutterstock, (Pie) Brand X Pictures/Thinkstock, (Cry) Photos to Go/Photolibrary, (Can) Thinkstock; **31** (Pan) Getty Images, (Fly) John Foxx/Thinkstock; **32** (Pan) Getty Images, (Fly) John Foxx/Thinkstock; **33** (Shop) ©Dmitriy Shironosov/Shutterstock, (Wheat) ©Zeljko Radojko/Shutterstock, (Hug) Creatas Images/Thinkstock, (Street) Siri Stafford/Thinkstock; **35** (Bug) Brand X Pictures/Thinkstock, (Beet) Photos to Go/Photolibrary, (Mop) Stockbyte/Thinkstock; **36** (Bug) Brand X Pictures/Thinkstock, (Beet) Photos to Go/Photolibrary, (Mop) Stockbyte/Thinkstock; **37** (Car) ©Adisa/Shutterstock, (Scrape) ©Marijus Auruskevicius/Shutterstock, (Smell) ©OJO Images Ltd./Alamy, (Well) ©Qwe Andersson/Alamy, (Bar) Creatas Images/Thinkstock, (Gate, Cape) Thinkstock; **39** (Crate) ©William Milner/Shutterstock, (Bell) Jupiter Images; **40** (Crate) ©William Milner/Shutterstock, (Bell) Jupiter Images; **41** (Plate) ©Artur Synenko/Shutterstock, (Goat, Fish) ©Eric Isselée/Shutterstock, (Fox) ©Jeremy Woodhouse/Getty Images, (Pail) ©Layland Masuda/Shutterstock, (Whale) ©Royalty-Free/Corbis, (Boat) ©ThinkStock/SuperStock, (Snake) Getty Images, (Mouse) Photos to Go/Photolibrary, (House) Thinkstock; **45** (Cub) ©Gontar/Shutterstock, (Pail) ©Layland Masuda/Shutterstock, (Bear) ©Eric Isselée/Shutterstock, (Whale) ©Royalty-Free/Corbis, (Tub) ©Vladislav Gajic/Shutterstock, (Duck) Shutterstock; **49** (Kite) ©D. Hurst/Alamy, (Crown) Corbis/Jupiter Images, (Drink) Goodshoot/Jupiter Images; **53** (Map) Digital Wisdom, Inc., (Bat) Getty Images, (Baby) Jupiter Images, (Barn) Shutterstock, (Mop, Bone) Stockbyte/Thinkstock, (Moon) Thinkstock; **55** (Bear) ©Eric Isselée/Shutterstock, (Mouse) Photos to Go/Photolibrary; **56** (Bear) ©Eric Isselée/Shutterstock, (Mouse) Photos to Go/Photolibrary; **57** (Roof) ©AbleStock/Index Open, (Road) ©Alexey Stiop/Shutterstock, (Sink) ©Simple Stock Shots, (Rope) ©Valzan/Shutterstock, (Seal) ImageShop/Jupiter Images; **59** (Saw) Getty Images; **60** (Saw) Getty Images; **61** (Road) ©Alexey Stiop/Shutterstock, (Mad) ©Brazhnykov Andriy/Shutterstock, (Boat) ©ThinkStock/SuperStock, (Bug) Brand X Pictures/Thinkstock, (Map) Digital Wisdom, Inc., (Saw) Getty Images, (Seal) ImageShop/Jupiter Images, (Mitt) Jupiter Images, (Mouse) Photos to Go/Photolibrary, (Mop) Stockbyte/Thinkstock, (Band) Thinkstock, (Soup) Thomas Northcut/Thinkstock; **63** (Saw) Getty Images, (Bell) Jupiter Images, (Mouse) Photos to Go/Photolibrary; **64** (Saw) Getty Images, (Bell) Jupiter Images, (Mouse) Photos to Go/Photolibrary; **73** (Goat) ©Eric Isselée/Shutterstock, (Tire) ©photolibrary/Index Open, (Game) ©Tatik22/Shutterstock, (Goose) Hemera Technologies, (Gold) Photodisc/Thinkstock, (Tooth) Shutterstock, (Gate) Thinkstock; **75** (Tiger) ©Smit/Shutterstock; **76** (Tiger) ©Smit/Shutterstock; **77** (Safety Pin) ©Ablestock/Index Open, (Pig) ©Anat-oli/Shutterstock, (Peach) ©Nikolai Pozdeev/Shutterstock, (Pie) Brand X Pictures/Thinkstock, (Nurse) Dynamic Graphics/Thinkstock, (Nail) Getty Images, (Nest) Jupiter Images, (Nap) Photos to Go/Photolibrary; **79** (Walnut) ©M. Unal Ozmen/Shutterstock, (Pot) ©Margouillat Photo/Shutterstock; **80** (Walnut) ©M. Unal Ozmen/Shutterstock, (Pot) ©Margouillat Photo/Shutterstock; **81** (Pig) ©Anat-oli/Shutterstock, (Goat) ©Eric Isselée/Shutterstock, (Pail) ©Layland Masuda/Shutterstock, (Pot) ©Margouillat Photo/Shutterstock, (Tire) ©photolibrary/Index Open, (Game) ©Tatik22/Shutterstock, (Tub) ©Vladislav Gajic/Shutterstock, (Nurse) Dynamic Graphics/Thinkstock, (Nail) Getty Images, (Goose) Hemera Technologies, (Gas) Hemera Technologies/Thinkstock, (Nest) Jupiter Images, (Tent) Shutterstock; **83** (Pig) ©Anat-oli/Shutterstock, (Tent) Shutterstock; **84** (Pig) ©Anat-oli/Shutterstock, (Tent) Shutterstock; **93** (Cart) ©Andrey Armyagov/Shutterstock, (Horse) ©Eric Isselée/Shutterstock, (Hat) ©Heath Doman/Shutterstock, (Cow) ©Jupiterimages/Brand X/Alamy, (Hot) ©Simone van den Berg/Alamy, (Hay, Ham, Cape, Can) Thinkstock; **95** (Hen) Getty Images; **96** (Hen) Getty Images; **97** (Fish) ©Eric Isselée/Shutterstock, (Fox) ©Jeremy Woodhouse/Getty Images, (Fire) Getty Images, (Feather) Jupiter Images, (Dive) Photos to Go/Photolibrary, (Duck) Shutterstock, (Deer) Thinkstock; **101** (Fish) ©Eric Isselée/Shutterstock, (Cow) ©Jupiterimages/Brand X/Alamy, (Door) ©Villedieu Christophe/Shutterstock, (Hen) Getty Images, (Corn) Jupiter Images, (Hill) Photos to Go/Photolibrary, (Horn) Shutterstock, (House) Thinkstock; **103** (Hen) Getty Images; **104** (Hen) Getty Images; **113** (Kite) ©D. Hurst/Alamy, (Leaf) ©Royalty-Free/Corbis, (Lion, Kitten, Kitchen , Kangaroo) Getty Images, (Lizard, King) Thinkstock; **115** (Log) ©Sebastian Knight/Shutterstock, (Kick) Rubberball Productions; **116** (Log) ©Sebastian Knight/Shutterstock, (Kick) Rubberball Productions; **117** (Waves, Eagle, Duck) Getty Images, (Jet) Photos to Go/Photolibrary, (Web) Thinkstock; **119** (Queen) Stockbyte/Thinkstock, (Jeep) Photos to Go; **120** (Queen) Stockbyte/Thinkstock, (Jeep) Photos to Go; **121** (Kite) ©D. Hurst/Alamy, (Leash) ©Konstantin Shevtsov/Shutterstock, (Well) ©Qwe Andersson/Alamy, (Kitten, Kangaroo) Getty Images, (Laugh) Photos to Go/Photolibrary, (Kick) Rubberball Productions, (Wet, Jumprope) Thinkstock; 133 (Violin) Getty Images, (Zoo, Yard) Photos to Go/Photolibrary, (Zebra) Shutterstock, (Vine) Thinkstock; **135** (Volcano) ©Stocktrek Images/Getty Images; **136** (Volcano) ©Stocktrek Images/Getty Images; **137** (Fox) ©Jeremy Woodhouse/Getty Images, (Cow) ©Jupiterimages/Brand X/Alamy, (Pot) ©Margouillat Photo/Shutterstock, (Wax) ©Sbarabu/Shutterstock, (Jet) Photos to Go/Photolibrary; **139** (Ax) ©Baloncici/Shutterstock, (Bat) Getty Images; **140** (Ax) ©Baloncici/Shutterstock, (Bat) Getty Images; **149** (Ship) ©DesignsPics/Index Open, (Horse) ©Eric Isselée/Shutterstock, (Hat) ©Heath Doman/Shutterstock, (Shark) ©Prochasson Frederic/Shutterstock, (Shovel, Sheep, Saw) Getty Images, (Seal) ImageShop/Jupiter Images, (House, Hay) Thinkstock; **151** (Shovel) Getty Images; **152** (Shovel) Getty Images; **153** (Horse) ©Eric Isselée/Shutterstock, (Hat) ©Heath Doman/Shutterstock, (Cow) ©Jupiterimages/Brand X/Alamy, (Chick) Getty Images, (Cherry) Photos to Go/Photolibrary, (Horn) Shutterstock, (House, Chimney, Can) Thinkstock; **157** (Shop) ©Dmitriy Shironosov/Shutterstock, (Horse) ©Eric Isselée/Shutterstock, (Hat) ©Heath Doman/Shutterstock, (Shark) ©Prochasson Frederic/Shutterstock, (Shovel, Sheep) Getty Images, (Cherry) Photos to Go/Photolibrary, (House, Hay, Chop, Chimney) Thinkstock; **159** (Shovel) Getty Images; **160** (Shovel) Getty Images; **161** (Thorn) ©Evgeni S./Shutterstock, (Wheelbarrow) ©James M. Phelps, Jr./Shutterstock, (Whale) ©Royalty-Free/Corbis, (Wheat) ©Zeljko Radojko/Shutterstock, (Thermos) Photos to Go/Photolibrary; **165** (Ship) ©DesignsPics/Index Open, (Thorn) ©Evgeni S./Shutterstock, (Wheelbarrow) ©James M. Phelps, Jr./Shutterstock, (Whale) ©Royalty-Free/Corbis, (Chick) Getty Images, (Thermos) Photos to Go/Photolibrary; **167** (Sheep) Getty Images; **168** (Sheep) Getty Images; 169 (Walnut) ©M. Unal Ozmen/Shutterstock, (Run) ©Monkey Business Images/Shutterstock, (Bug) Brand X Pictures/Thinkstock, (Map) Digital Wisdom, Inc., (Pan, Hen, Bat) Getty Images, (Jet) Photos to Go/Photolibrary, (Mop) Stockbyte/Thinkstock; **170** (Pig) ©Anat-oli/Shutterstock, (Kite) ©D. Hurst/Alamy, (Goat, Fish) ©Eric Isselée/Shutterstock, (Map) Digital Wisdom, Inc., (Saw) Getty Images, (Nest) Jupiter Images, (Jet) Photos to Go/Photolibrary, (Web, Ham) Thinkstock; **171** (Dad) ©Corbis, (Hat) ©Heath Doman/Shutterstock, (Hog) ©Tim Burrett/Shutterstock, (Bug) Brand X Pictures/Thinkstock, (Map) Digital Wisdom, Inc., (Cot) Hemera Technologies/Thinkstock, (Jet, Hill) Photos to Go/Photolibrary, (Mop) Stockbyte/Thinkstock, (Rip) Thinkstock; **172** (Ship) ©DesignsPics/Index Open, (Thorn) ©Evgeni S./Shutterstock, (Whale) ©Royalty-Free/Corbis, (Wheat) ©Zeljko Radojko/Shutterstock, (Sheep, Chick) Getty Images, (Thermos, Cherry) Photos to Go/Photolibrary

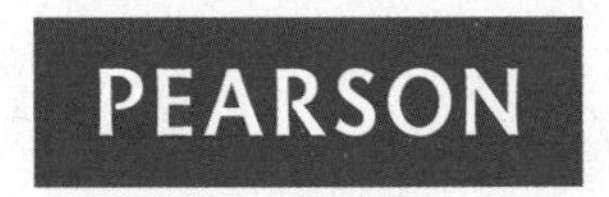

ISBN-13: 978-1-4284-3132-4
ISBN-10: 1-4284-3132-2
11 12 13 14 15 V011 19 18 17 16 15

Contents

Sort 1 Concept Sort **Fruit/Not a Fruit** 1

Sort 2 Concept Sort **Animal/Not an Animal** 5

Sort 3 Concept Sort **Shapes** 9

Sort 4 Concept Sort **Food, Clothes, Toys** 13

Sort 5 Concept Sort **Clothes** 17

Sort 6 Concept Sort **Food** 21

Sort 7 Rhyming Sort **Nose, Knees, Hair, Head** 25

Sort 8 Rhyming Sort **Clock, Fly, Pan** 29

Sort 9 Rhyming Sort **Bug, Mop, Beet** 33

Sort 10 Rhyming Sort **Jar, Crate, Bell, Grape** 37

Sort 11 Rhyming Sort **Pairs 1** 41

Sort 12 Rhyming Sort **Pairs 2** 45

Sort 13 Rhyming Sort **Colors** 49

Sort 14 Beginning Sounds **b, m** 53

Sort 15 Beginning Sounds **r, s** 57

Sort 16 Beginning Sounds **b, m, r, s** 61

Sort 17 Letter Recognition **Bb, Mm, Aa** 65

Sort 18 Letter Recognition **Rr, Ss, Ee** 69

Sort 19 Beginning Sounds **t, g** 73

Sort 20 Beginning Sounds **n, p** 77

Sort 21 Beginning Sounds **t, g, n, p** 81

Sort 22 Letter Recognition **Tt, Gg, Ee** 85

Sort 23 Letter Recognition **Nn, Pp, Ii** 89

Sort 24 Beginning Sounds **c, h** 93

Sort 25 Beginning Sounds **f, d** 97

Sort 26 Beginning Sounds **c, h, f, d** 101

Sort 27 Letter Recognition **Cc, Hh, Ii** 105

Sort 28 Letter Recognition **Ff, Dd, Aa** 109

Sort 29 Beginning Sounds **l, k** 113

Sort 30 Beginning Sounds **j, w, q** 117

Sort 31 Beginning Sounds **l, k, j, w** 121

Sort 32 Letter Recognition **Ll, Kk, Oo** 125

Sort 33 Letter Recognition **Jj, Ww, Qq** 129

Sort 34 Beginning Sounds **y, z, v** 133

Sort 35 Ending Sounds **t, x** 137

Sort 36 Letter Recognition **Yy, Zz, Vv** ... 141

Sort 37 Letter Recognition **Tt, Xx, Uu** ... 145

Sort 38 **s**, **h**, and Digraph **sh** 149

Sort 39 **c**, **h**, and Digraph **ch** 153

Sort 40 **h** and Digraphs **sh** and **ch** 157

Sort 41 Digraphs **th, wh** 161

Sort 42 Digraphs **sh, ch, wh, th** 165

Spell Check 1: Rhyming Words 169

Spell Check 2: Beginning Consonants ... 170

Spell Check 3: Letter Recognition 171

Spell Check 4: Digraphs 172

Concept Sort Fruit/Not a Fruit

Draw two fruits and two things that are not fruits. Write the word below each picture.

Draw two animals and two things that are not animals. Write the word below each picture.

▲	●	■

Draw two triangles, two circles, and two squares.

▲	●	■

P
J
S

Concept Sort Food, Clothes, Toys

Draw two kinds of food, two kinds of clothes, and two toys. Write the word below each picture.

Concept Sort **Clothes**

Draw one thing you can wear on your head, one thing you can wear on your feet, one thing you can wear on your body, and one thing you can wear on your hands. Write the word below each picture.

Concept Sort Clothes

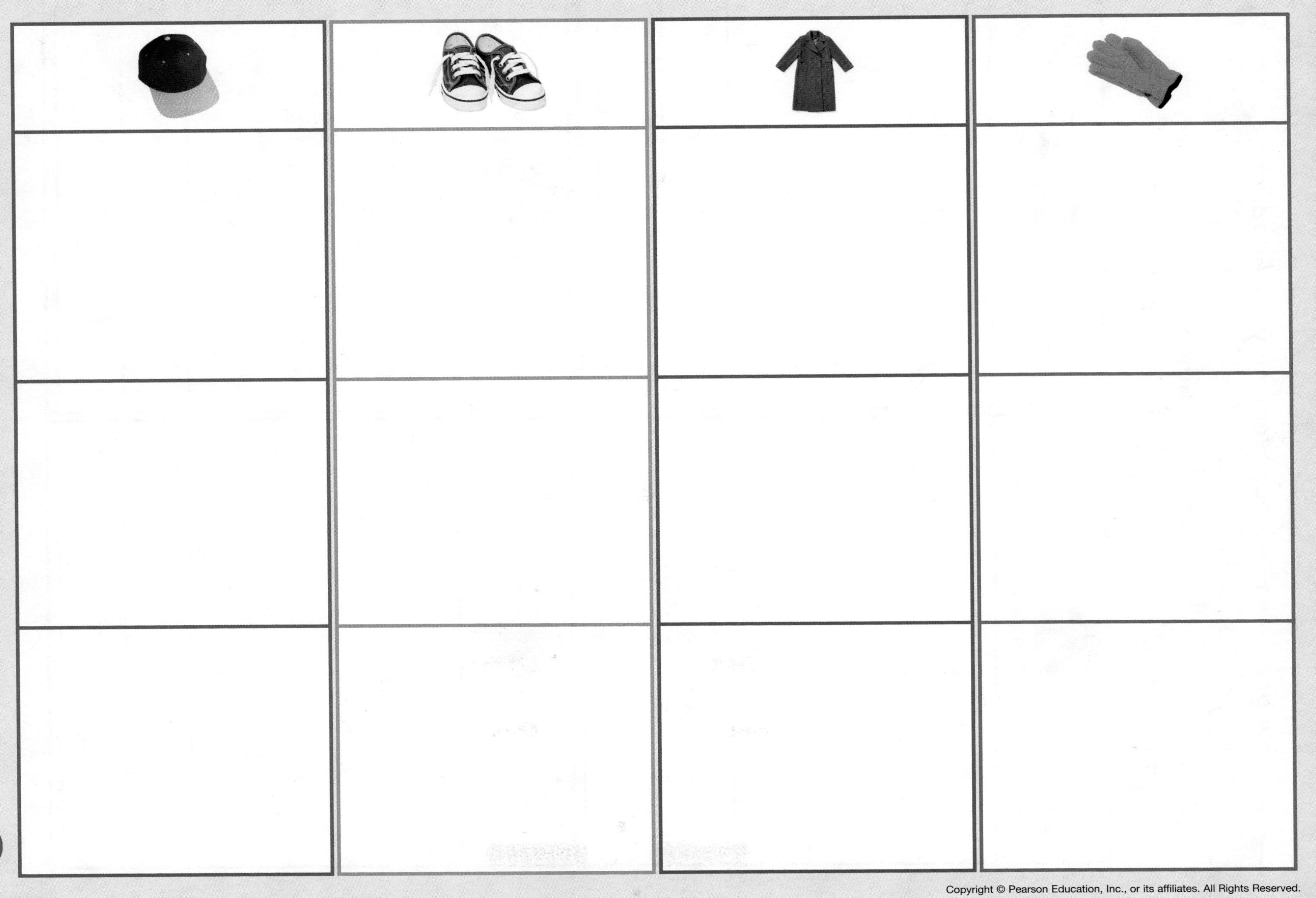

Draw one thing you can wear on your head, one thing you can wear on your feet, one thing you can wear on your body, and one thing you can wear on your hands. Write the word below each picture.

Concept Sort Food

Draw one bread, one beverage, one fruit, and one vegetable. Write the word below each picture.

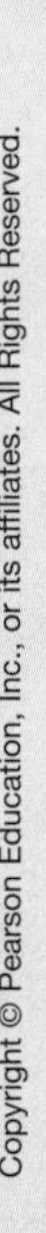

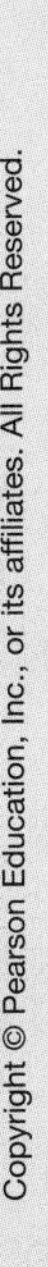

Rhyming Sort Nose, Knees, Hair, Head

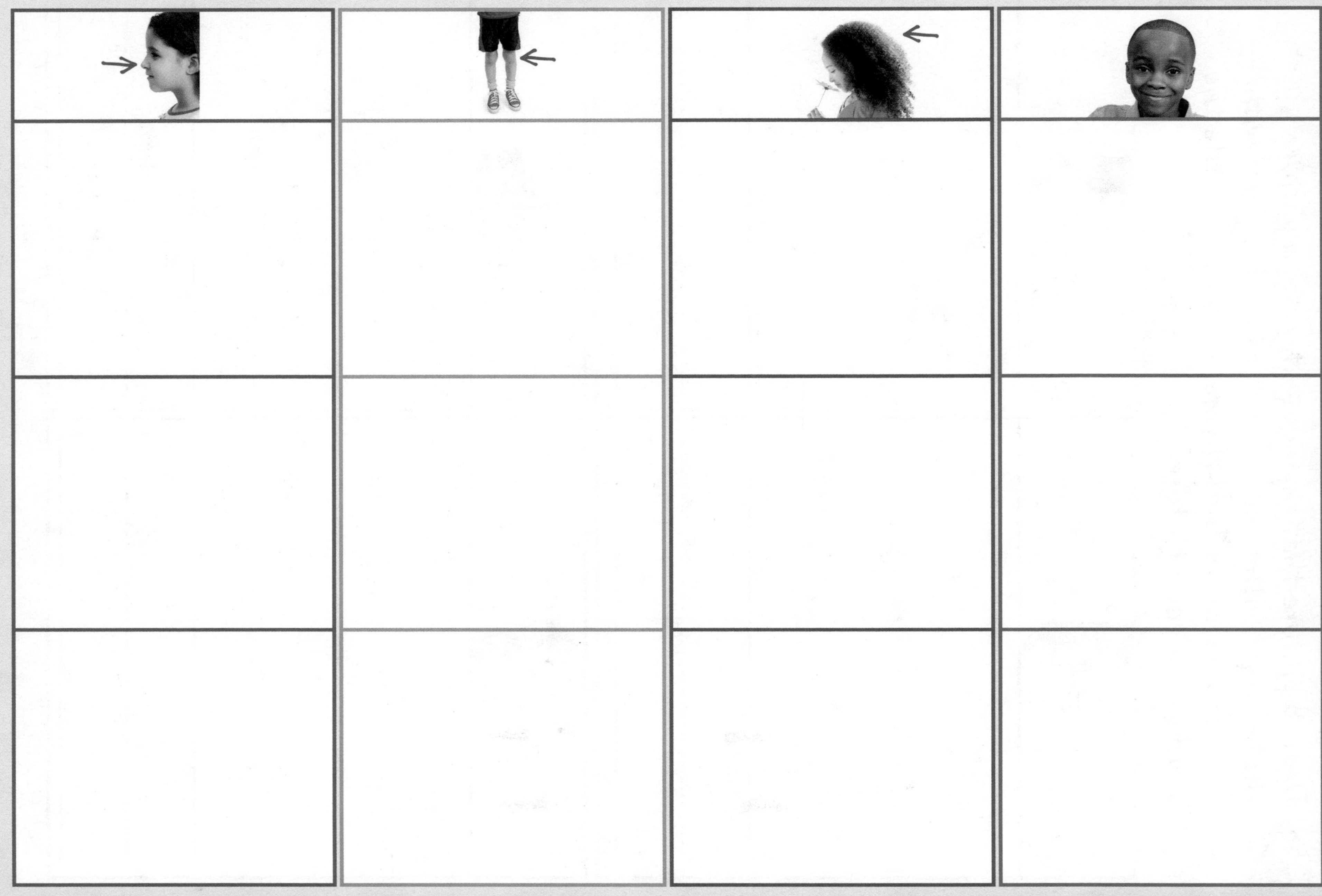

Draw a picture that rhymes with nose, a picture that rhymes with knees, a picture that rhymes with hair, and a picture that rhymes with head. Write the word below each picture.

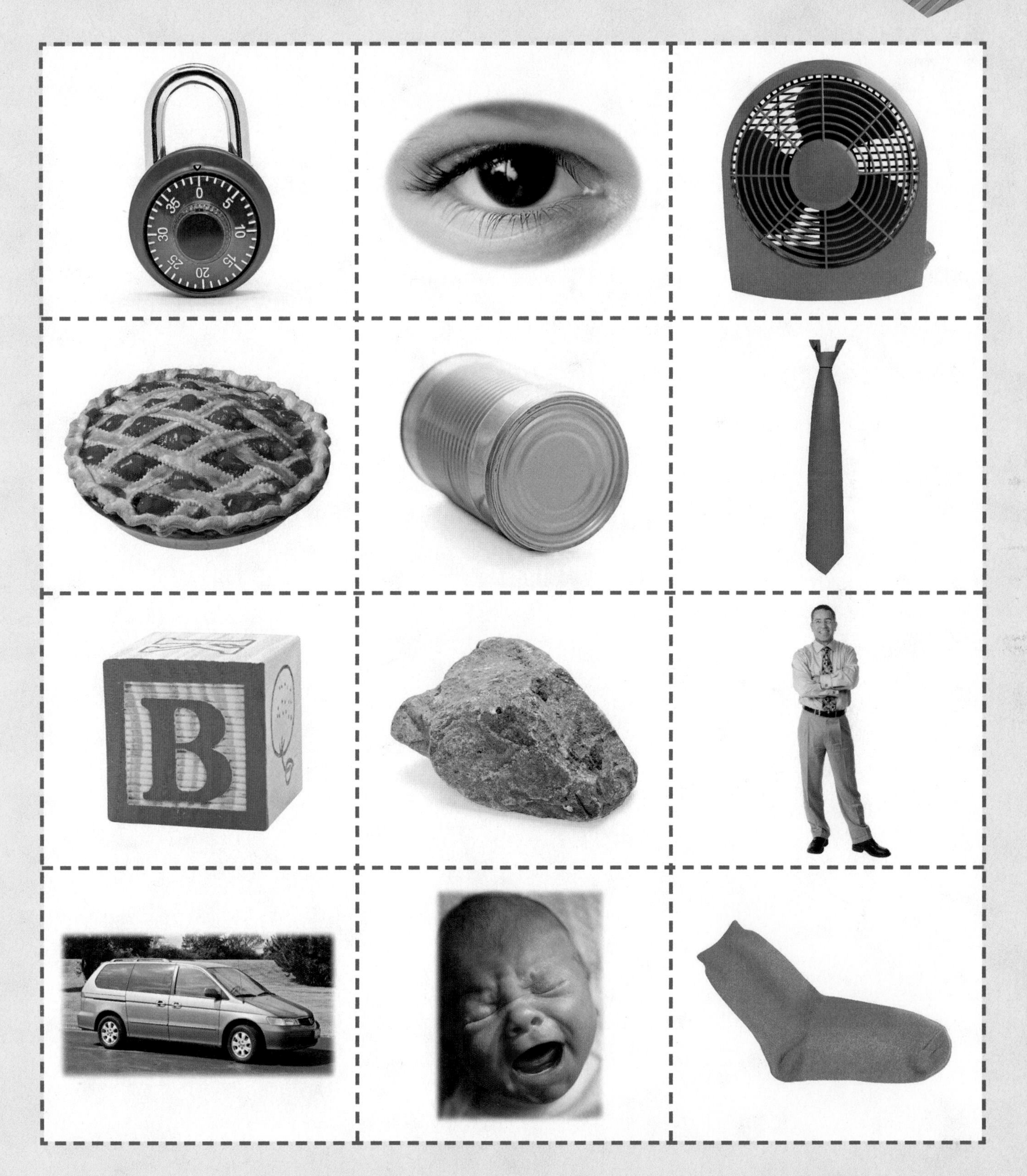
0
5
10
15
20
25
30
35
B

Rhyming Sort Clock, Fly, Pan

Draw pictures of two things that rhyme with clock, two things that rhyme with fly, and two things that rhyme with pan. Write the word below each picture.

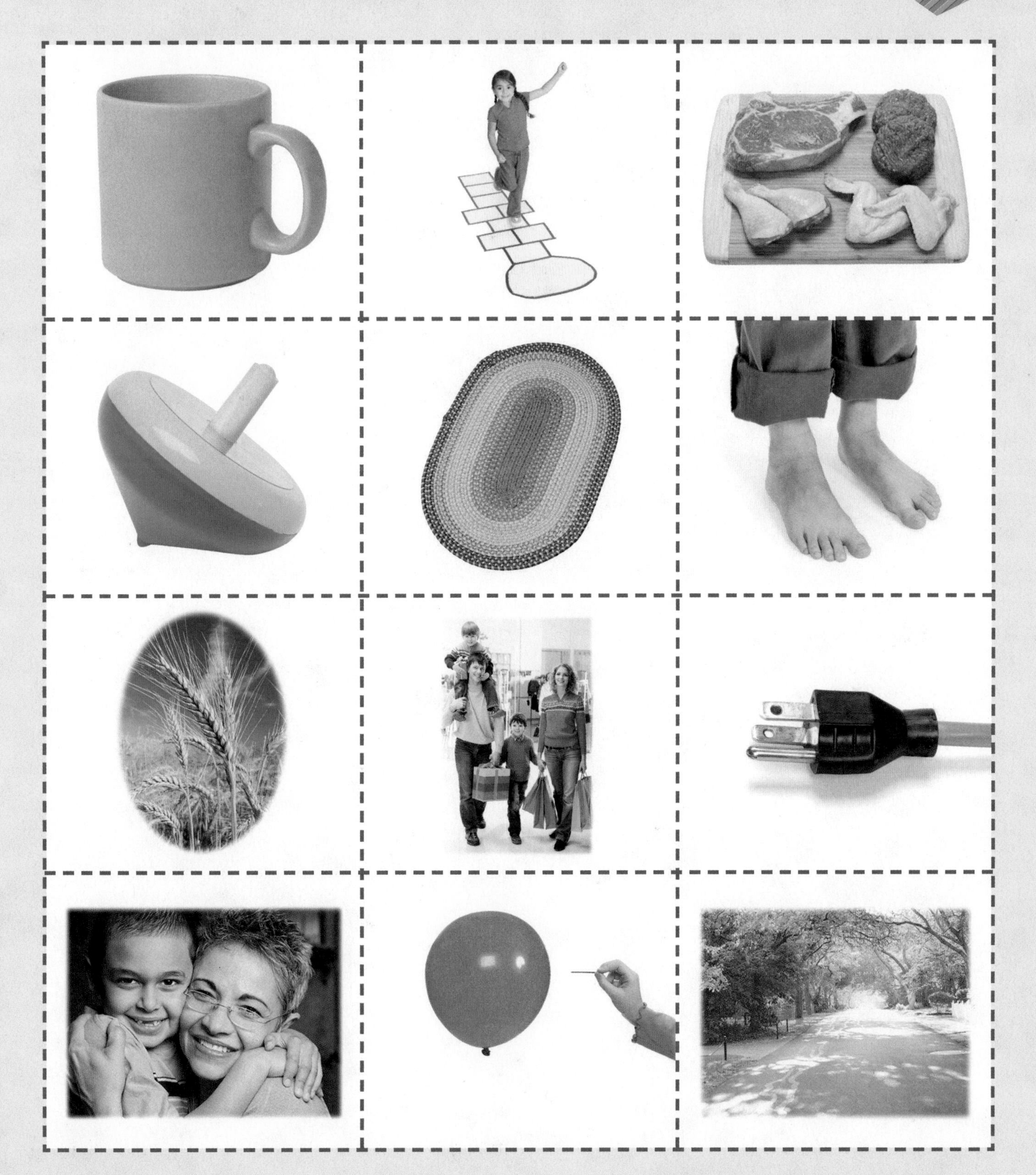

Rhyming Sort **Bug, Mop, Beet**

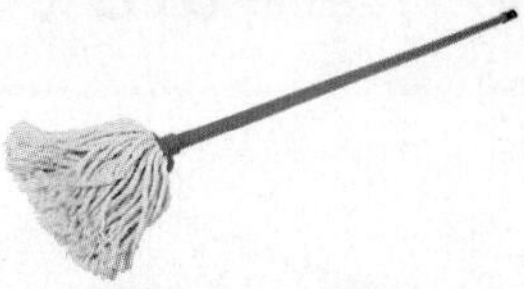

Draw pictures of two things that rhyme with bug, two things that rhyme with mop, and two things that rhyme with beet. Write the word below each picture.

Rhyming Sort Jar, Crate, Bell, Grape

Draw a picture that rhymes with jar, a picture that rhymes with crate, a picture that rhymes with bell, and a picture that rhymes with grape. Write the word below each picture.

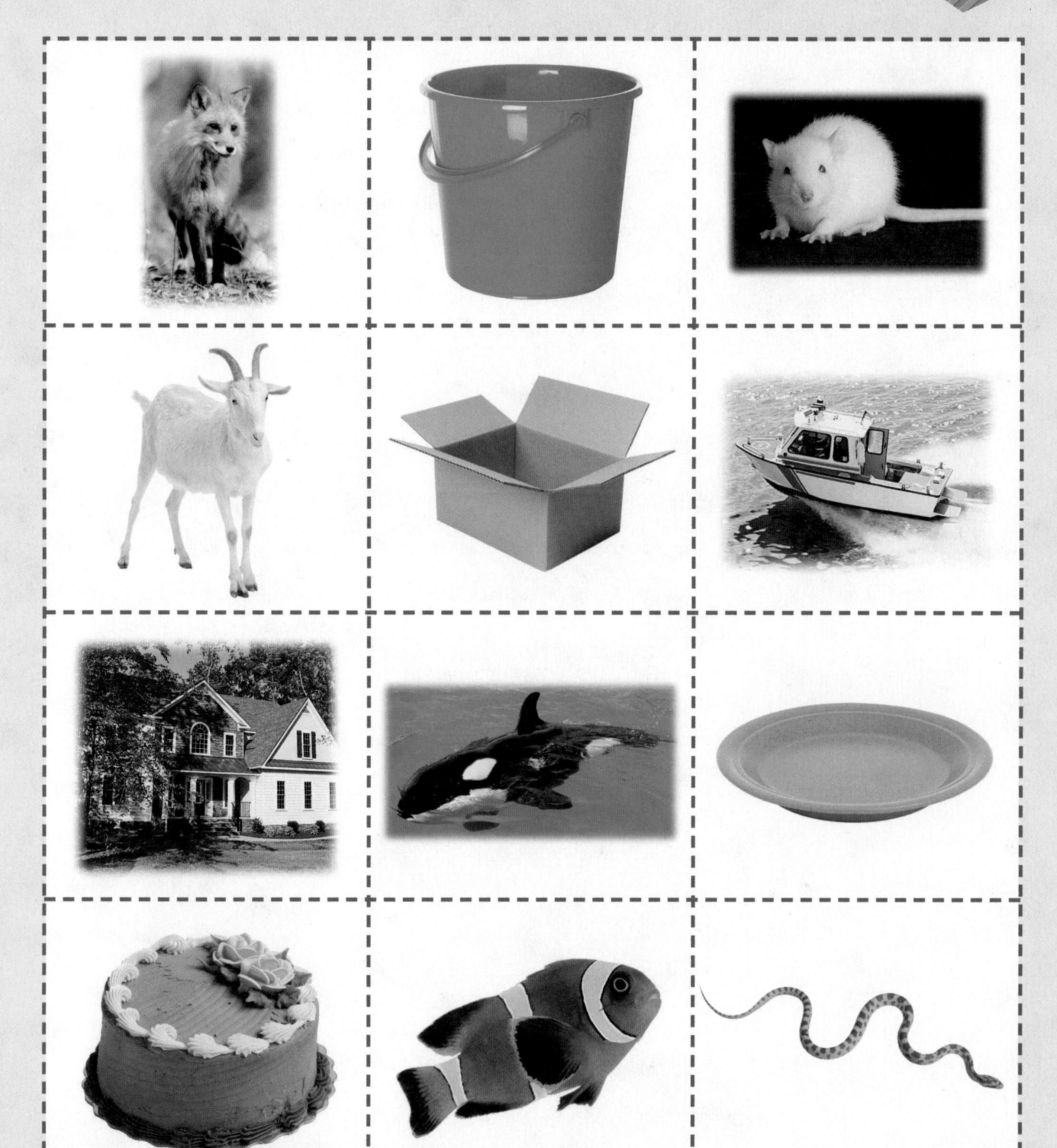

Draw two sets of things that rhyme.
Write the word below each picture.

Rhyming Sort Pairs 2

Draw two sets of things that rhyme.
Write the word below each picture.

Draw two sets of things that rhyme.
Write the word below each picture.

Sort
14

Bb		Mm	

Draw pictures of two things that begin with Bb and Mm. Write the word below each picture.

Bb	Mm

Beginning Sounds r, s

Rr	Ss

Draw pictures of two things that begin with Rr and Ss. Write the word below each picture.

Rr	Ss

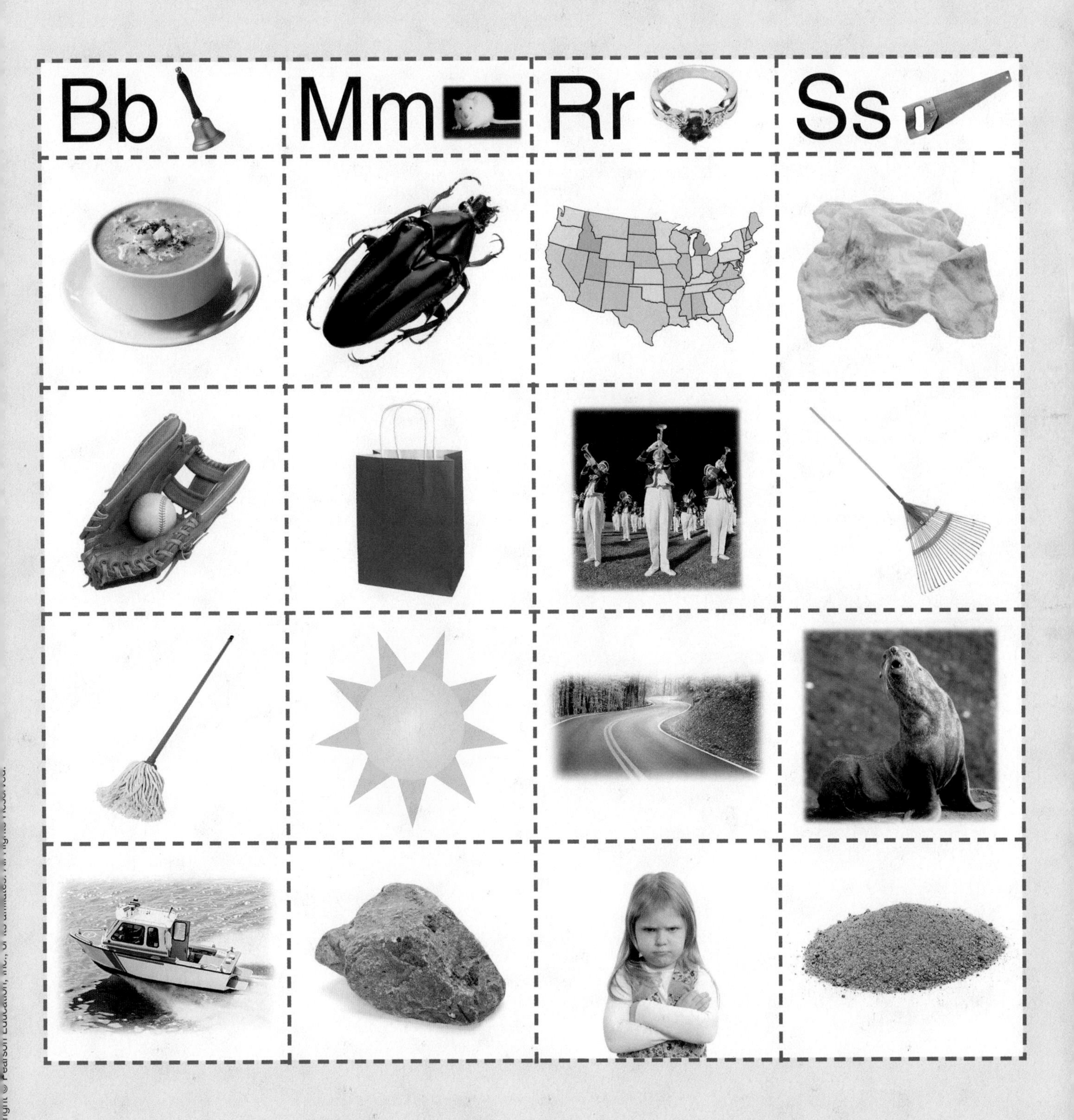
Bb
Mm
Rr
Ss

Bb	Mm	Rr	Ss

Draw a picture of one thing that begins with Bb, Mm, Rr, and Ss. Write the word below each picture.

Bb	Mm
Rr	**Ss**

M	a	b	m
B	A	m	a
M	M	b	B
A	B	M	m
b	B	A	b
a	m	a	A

Bb		Mm		Aa	

Say the name of each letter. Then print each letter on the lines.

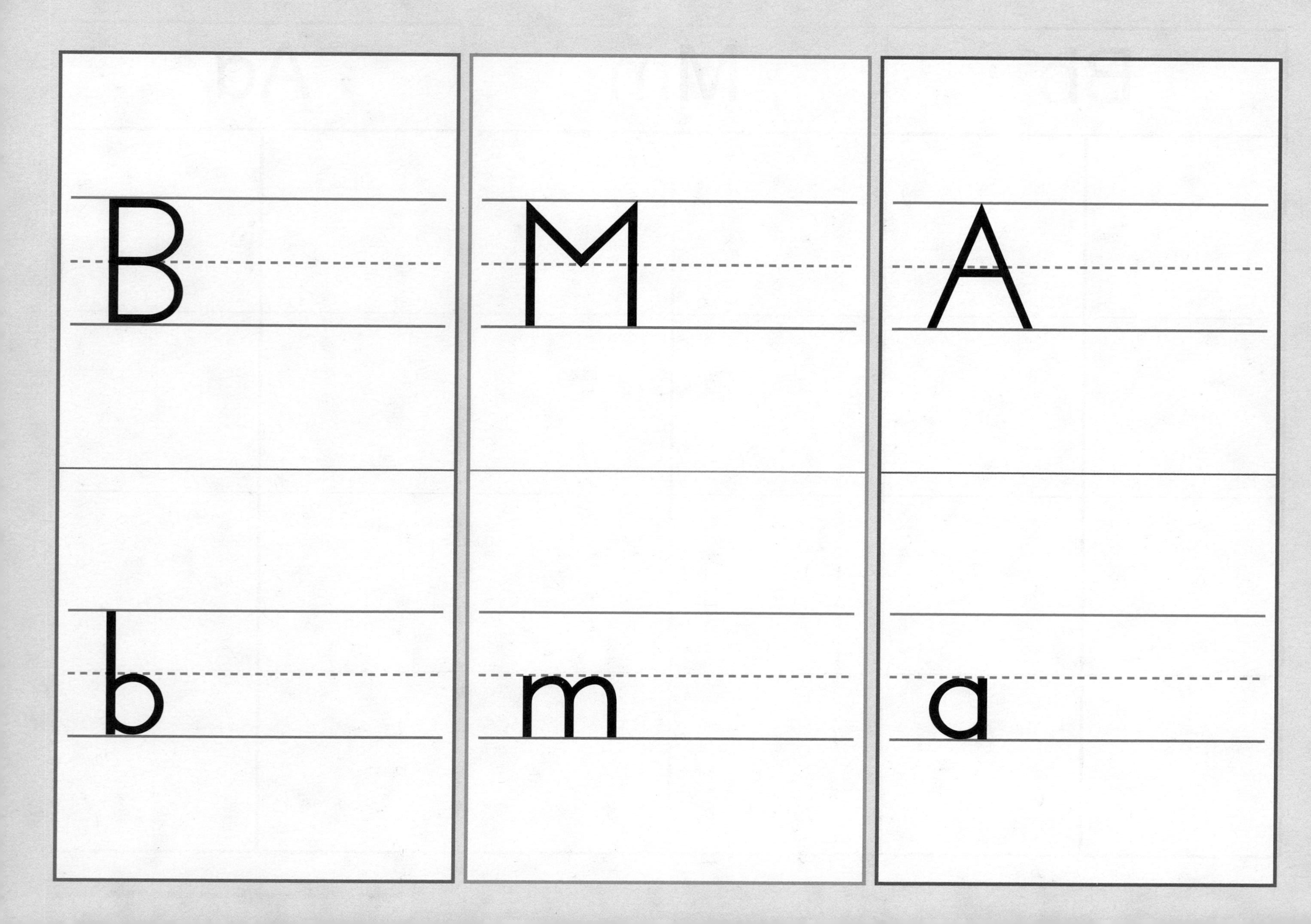

E	s	S	S
R	e	R	r
s	E	r	e
S	E	R	s
e	s	E	r
r	e	R	S

Rr		Ss		Ee	

Say the name of each letter. Then print each letter on the lines.

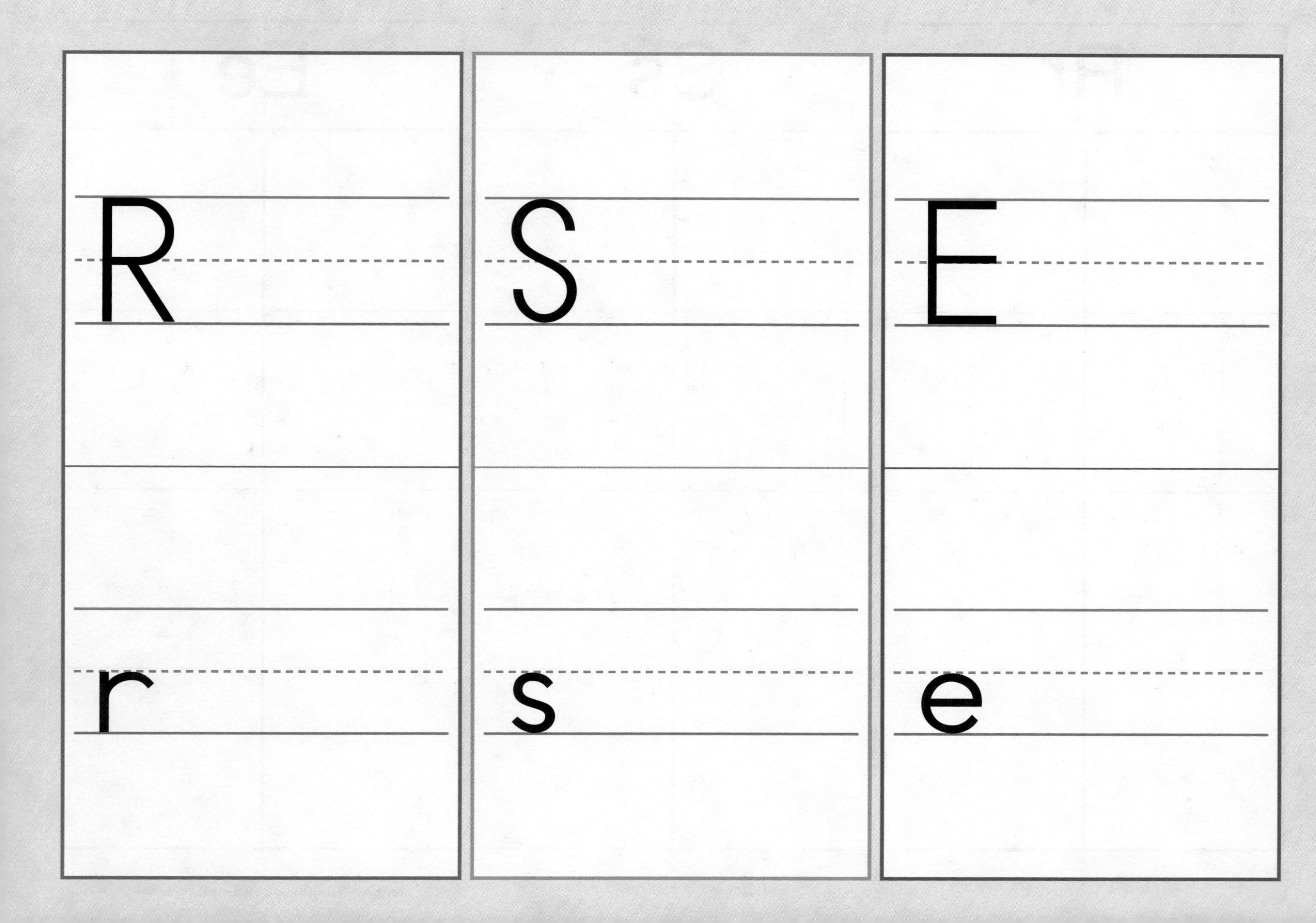

Beginning Sounds t, g

Tt	Gg

Draw pictures of two things that begin with Tt and Gg. Write the word below each picture.

Tt	Gg

Pp

Nn

Draw pictures of two things that begin with Nn and Pp. Write the word below each picture.

Nn	Pp

Tt
Gg
Nn
Pp

Tt	Gg	Nn	Pp

Draw a picture that begins with Tt, Gg, Nn, and Pp.
Write the word below each picture.

Tt	Gg

Nn	Pp

T	g	E	e
E	e	T	t
e	g	t	G
G	E	t	E
t	g	G	T
G	g	T	e

Tt

Gg

Ee

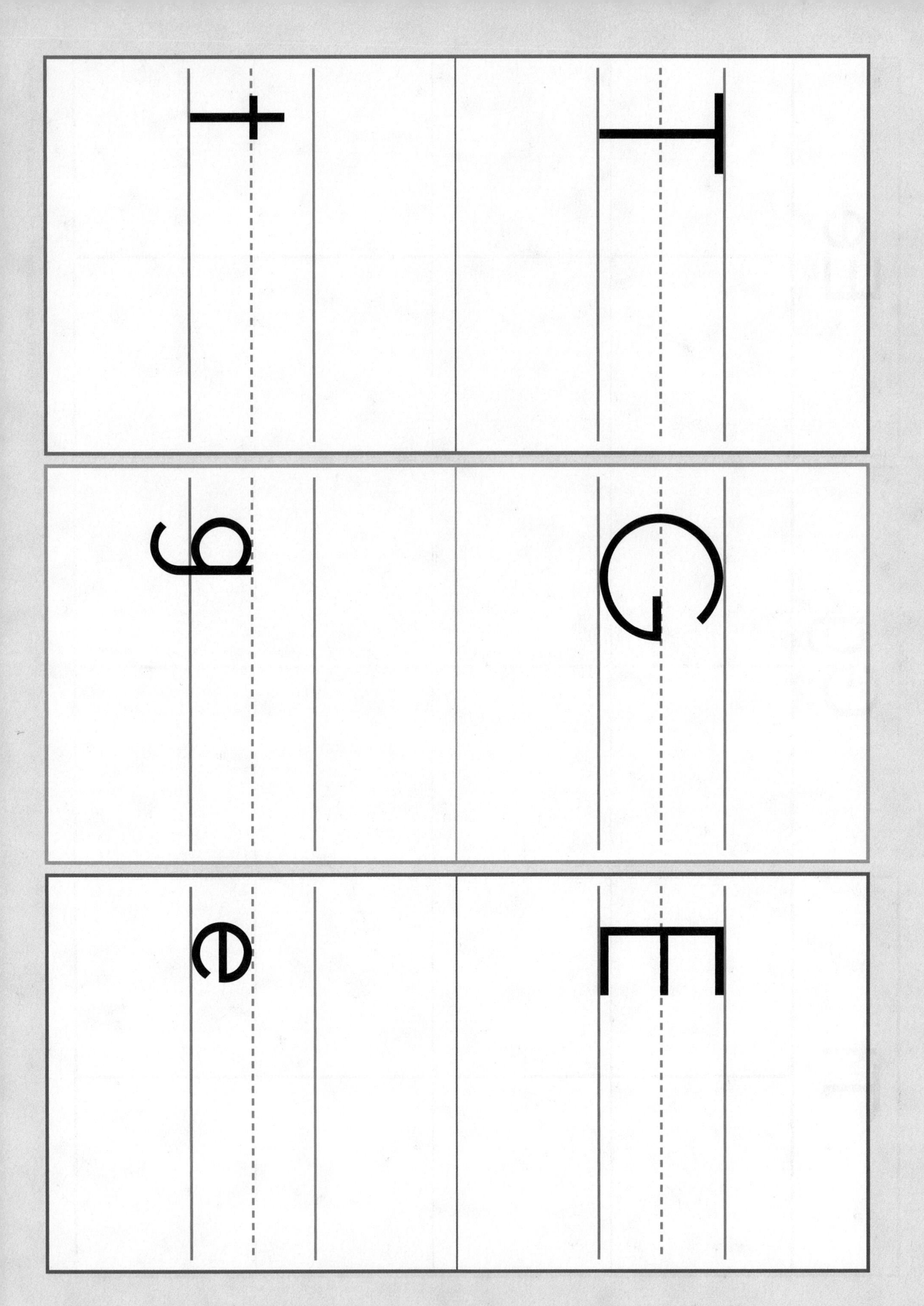
t
T
g
G
e
E

i	N	P	n
n	p	I	i
I	n	N	p
I	P	p	N
P	n	I	p
i	N	p	i

Nn	Pp	Ii

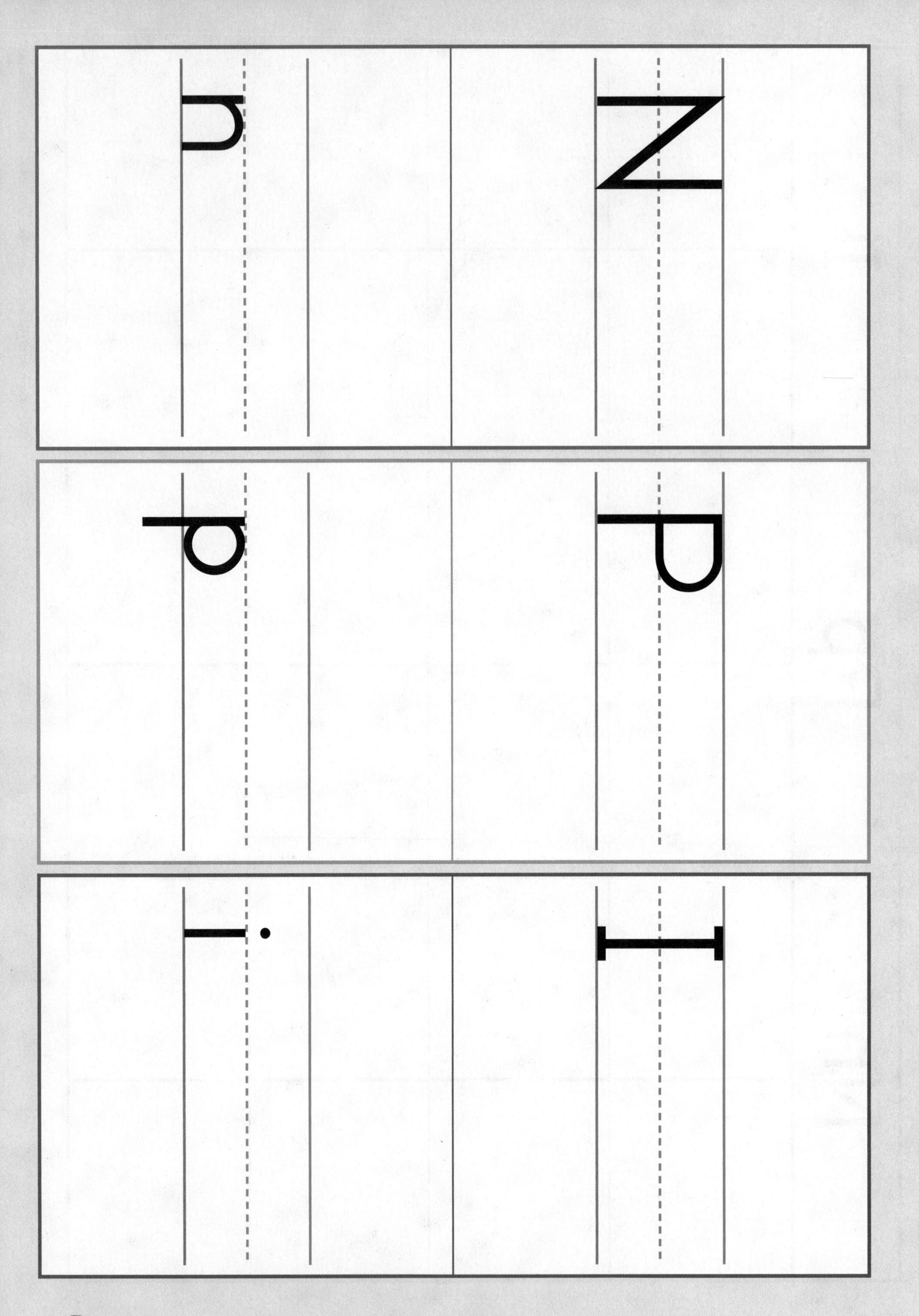
n
N
p
P
i
I

Hh		

Cc		

Draw pictures of two things that begin with Cc and Hh. Write the word below each picture.

Cc	Hh

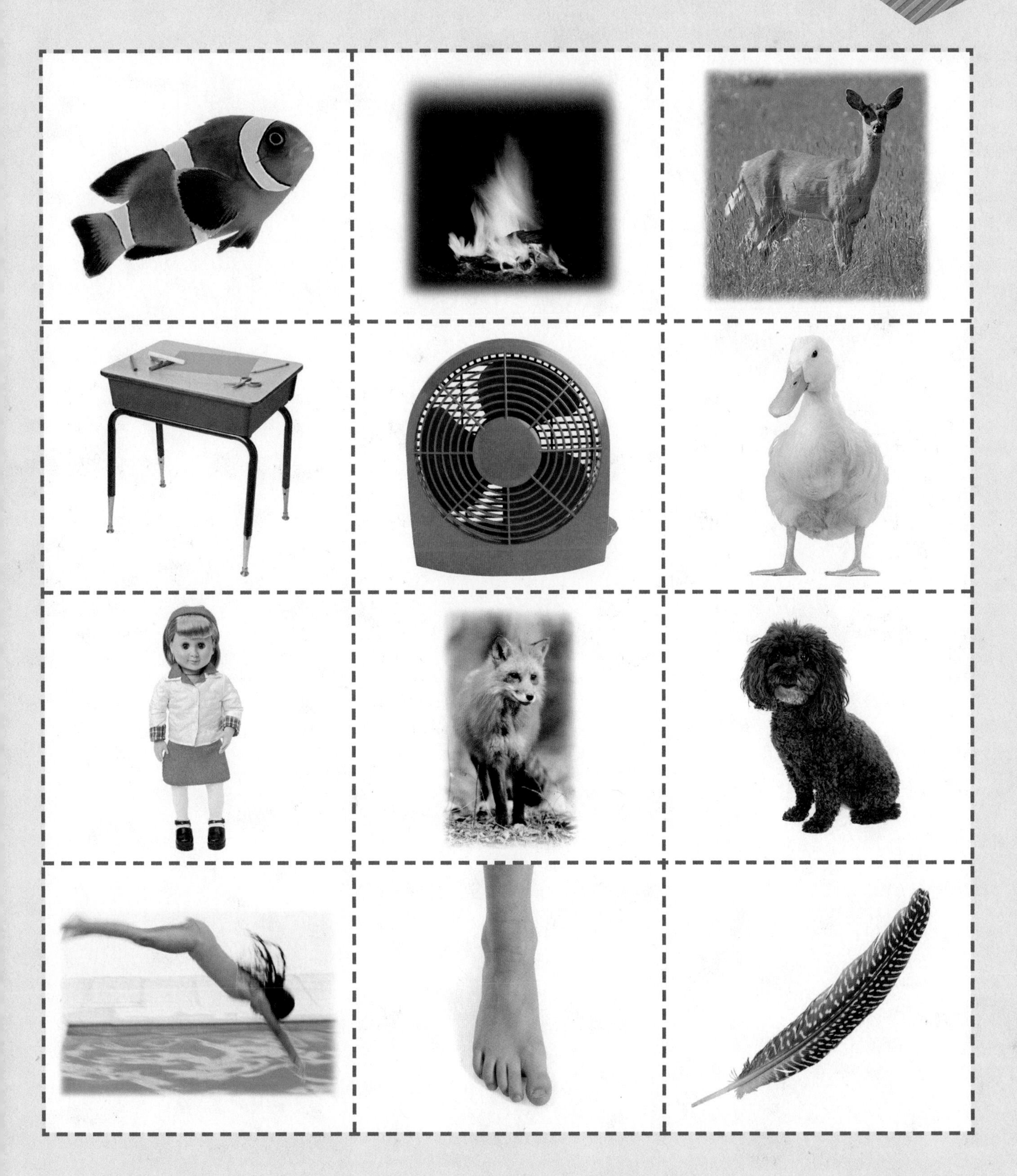

Dd

Ff

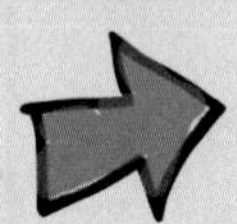

Draw pictures of two things that begin with Ff and Dd. Write the word below each picture.

Ff	Dd

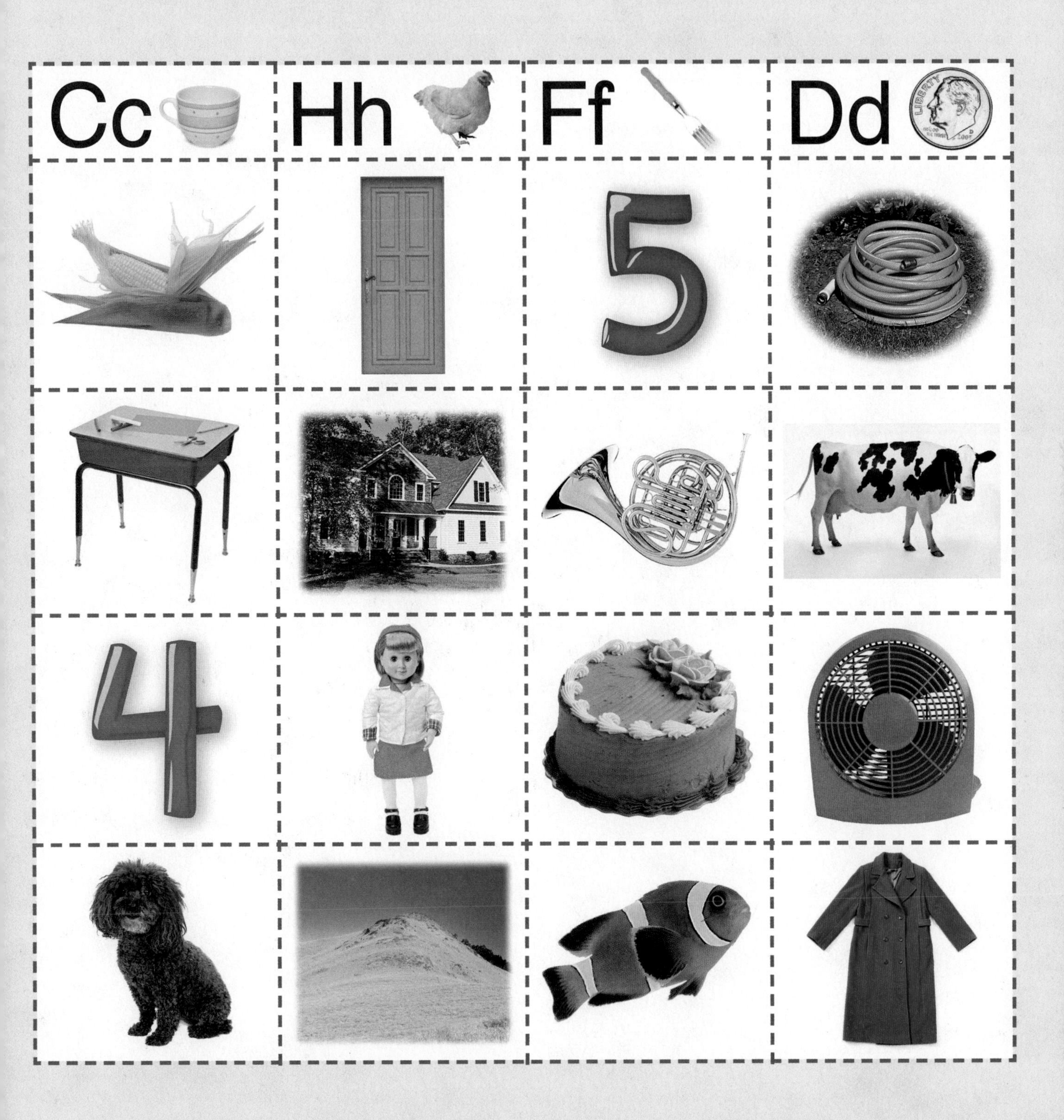
Cc
Hh
Ff
Dd
LIBERTY

Cc	Hh	Ff	Dd

Draw a picture that begins with Cc, Hh, Ff, and Dd.
Write the word below each picture.

Cc	Hh
Ff	**Dd**

c	h	H	C
C	I	i	h
c	I	H	H
i	h	c	I
i	H	C	i
c	h	I	c

Cc	Hh	Ii

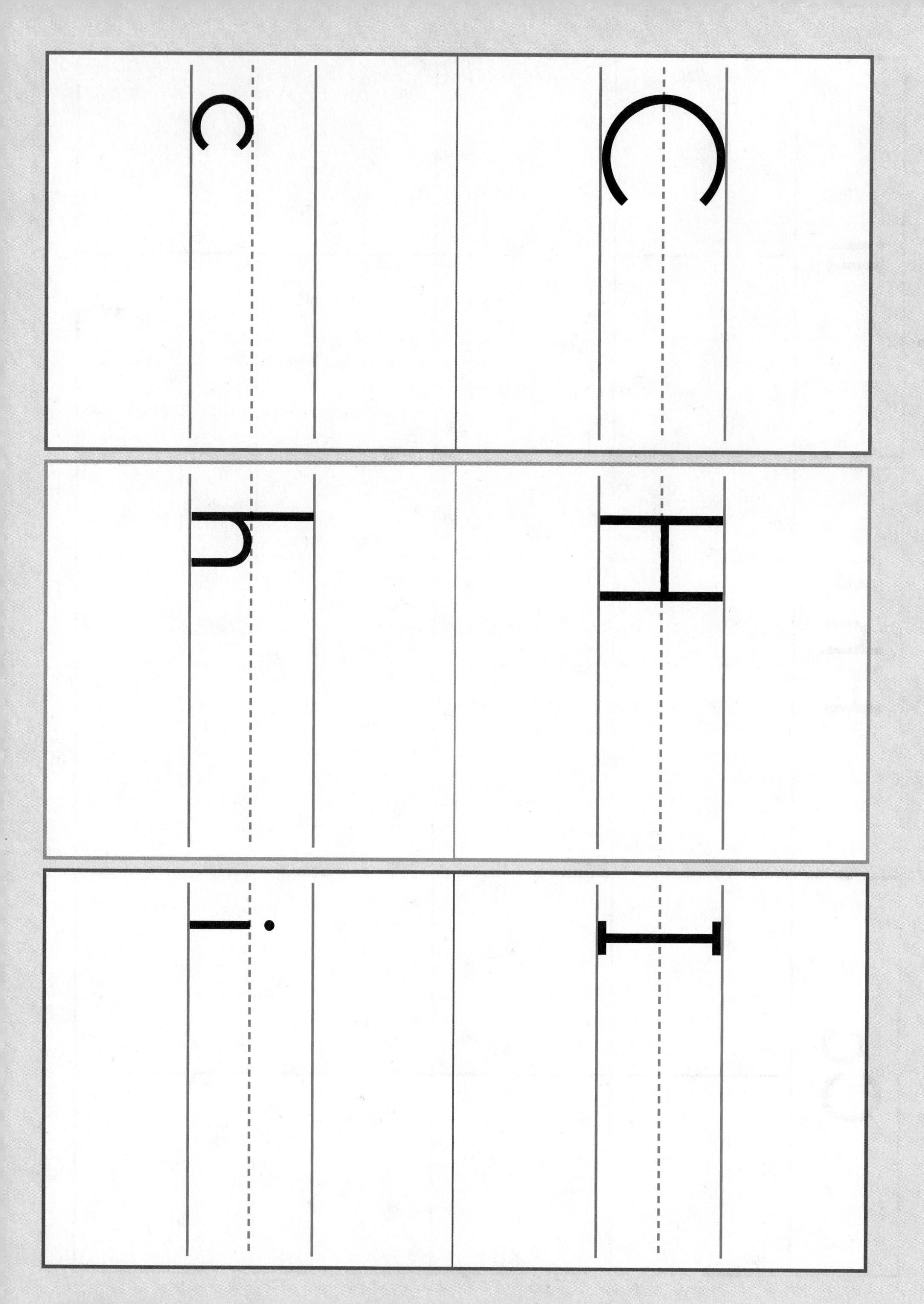

d	F	D	f
d	F	D	A
A	f	F	D
a	A	D	d
A	f	a	F
f	a	d	a

Ff		Dd		Aa	

Say the name of each letter. Then print each letter on the lines.

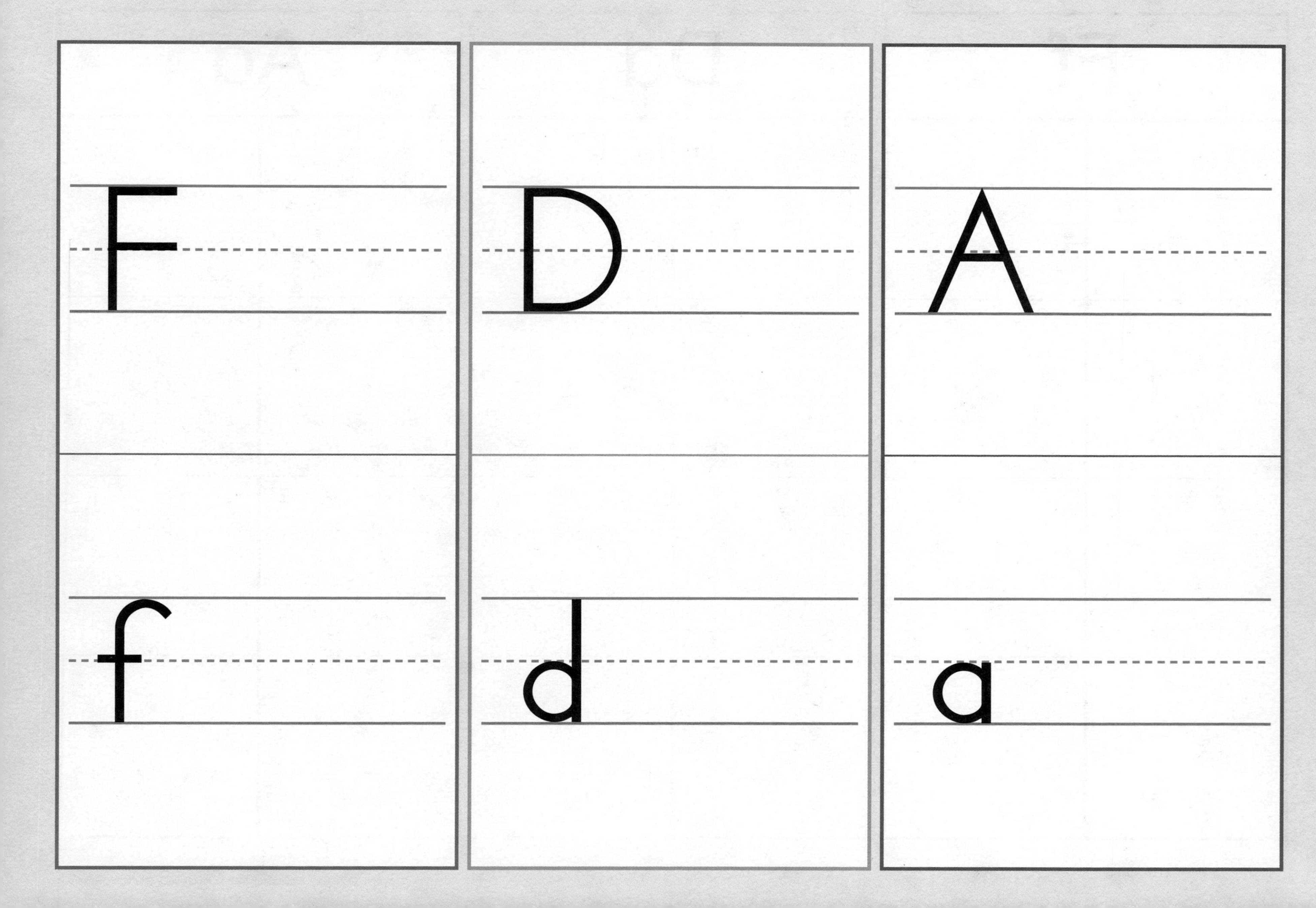

35
0
5
30
10
25
20
15

Ll	Kk

Draw pictures of two things that begin with Ll and Kk. Write the word below each picture.

Ll	Kk

UNITED STATES OF AMERICA
LIBERTY
IN GOD WE TRUST
QUARTER DOLLAR

Jj	Ww	Qq

Draw pictures of two things that begin with Jj, Ww, and Qq. Write the word below each picture.

Jj	Ww	Qq

Sort 31

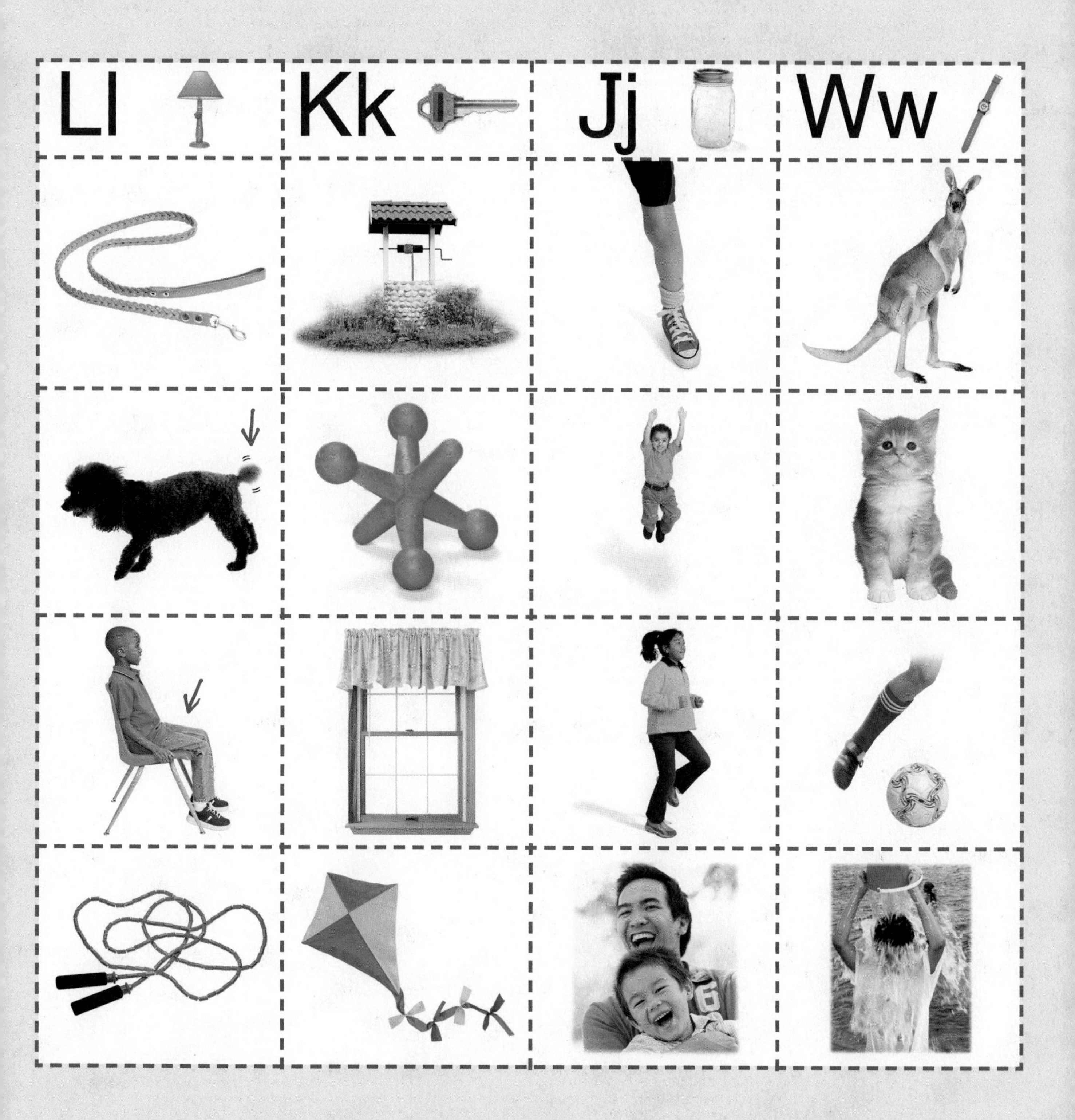

Ll	Kk	Jj	Ww

Draw a picture that begins with Ll, Kk, Jj, and Ww.
Write the word below each picture.

Ll	Kk

Jj	Ww

K	L	k	K
l	o	O	l
o	L	K	O
L	l	k	l
O	K	o	O
k	L	o	k

Ll	Kk	Oo

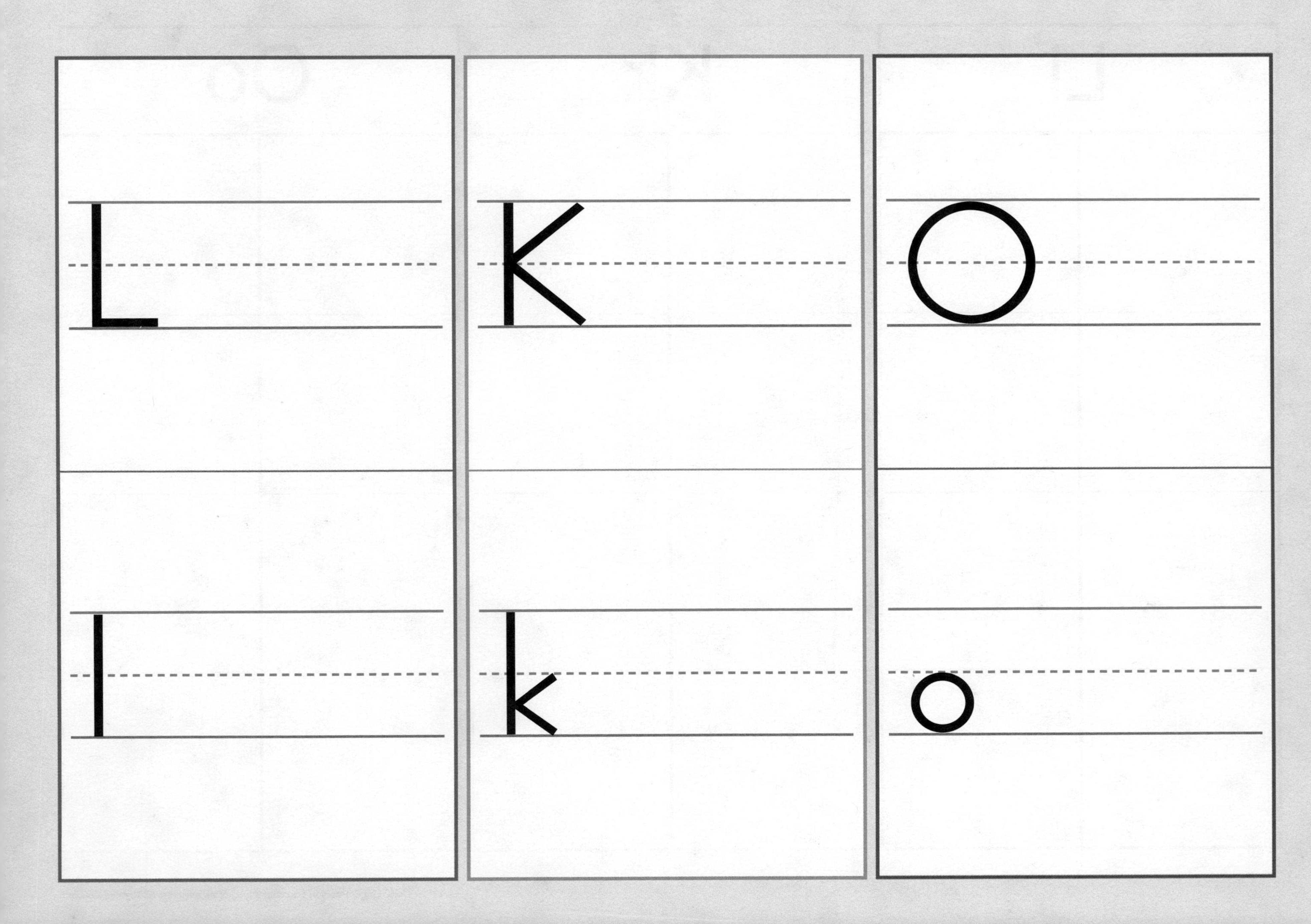
L
K
O
l
k
o

W	J	q	w
j	w	J	j
J	Q	j	Q
q	W	j	w
q	J	W	Q
W	q	Q	W

Jj	Ww	Qq

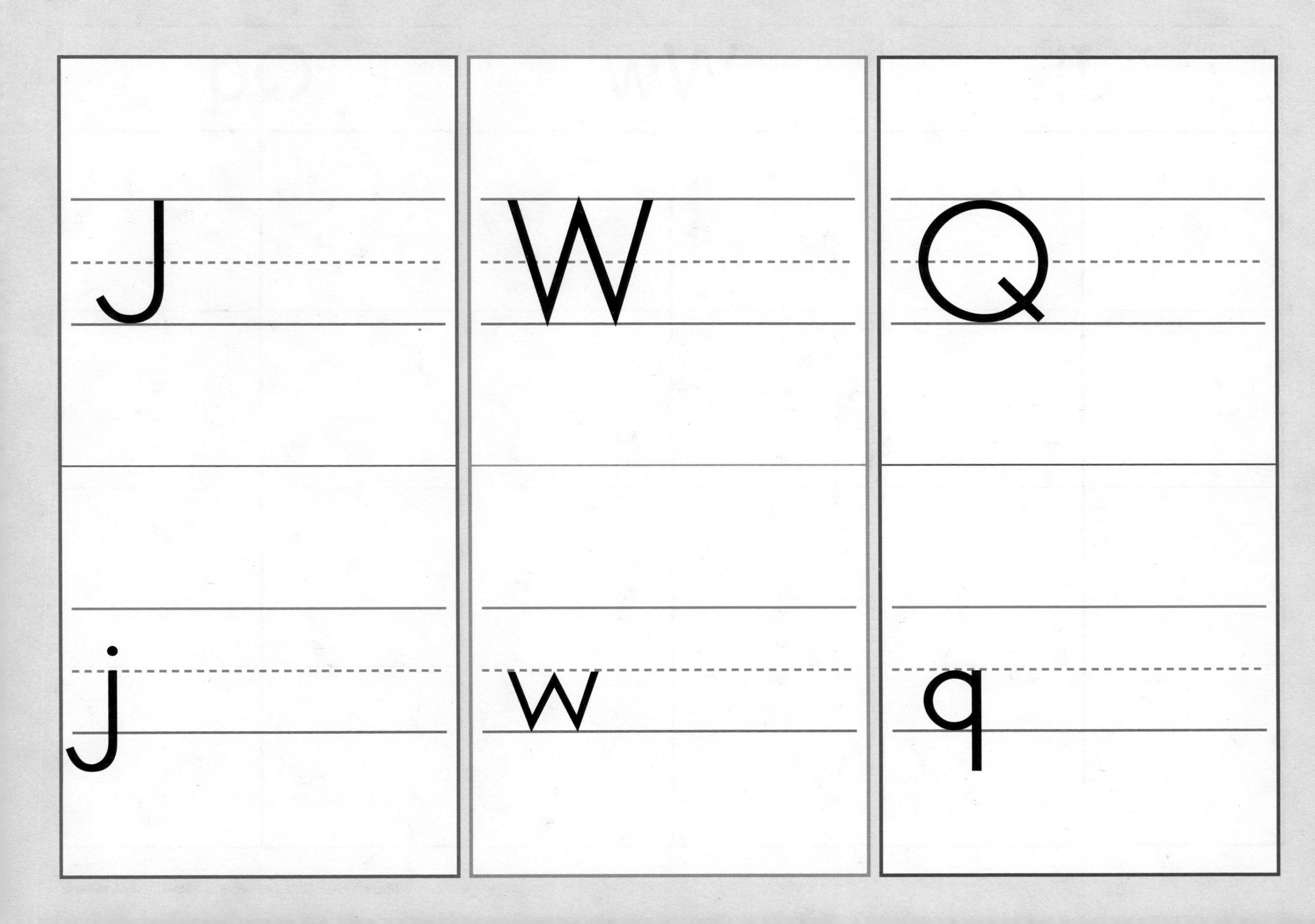
J
W
Q
j
w
q

YOGURT
Blueberry

Yy	Zz	Vv

Draw pictures of two things that begin with Yy, Zz, and Vv. Write the word below each picture.

Yy	Zz	Vv

bat	ax

Draw pictures of two things that end with Tt and Xx. Write the word below each picture.

bat	ax

y	Z	v	Y
z	y	V	Z
v	Z	Y	V
Y	V	z	z
z	y	v	Y
V	Z	Y	v

Yy	Zz	Vv

Say the name of each letter. Then print each letter on the lines.

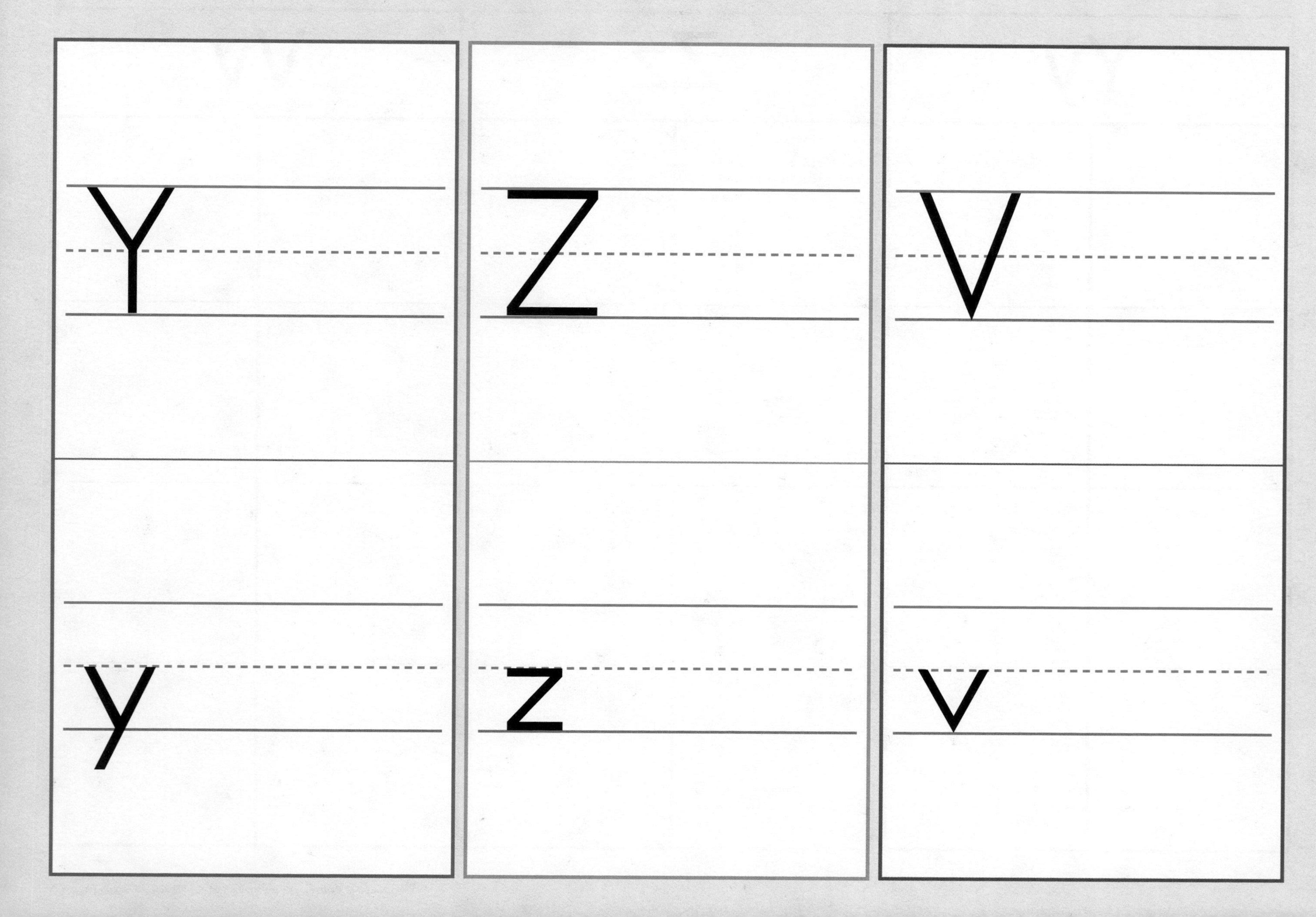

t	U	x	t
u	t	X	U
x	U	T	X
T	X	u	u
u	t	x	T
X	U	T	x

Tt	Xx	Uu

Say the name of each letter. Then print each letter on the lines.

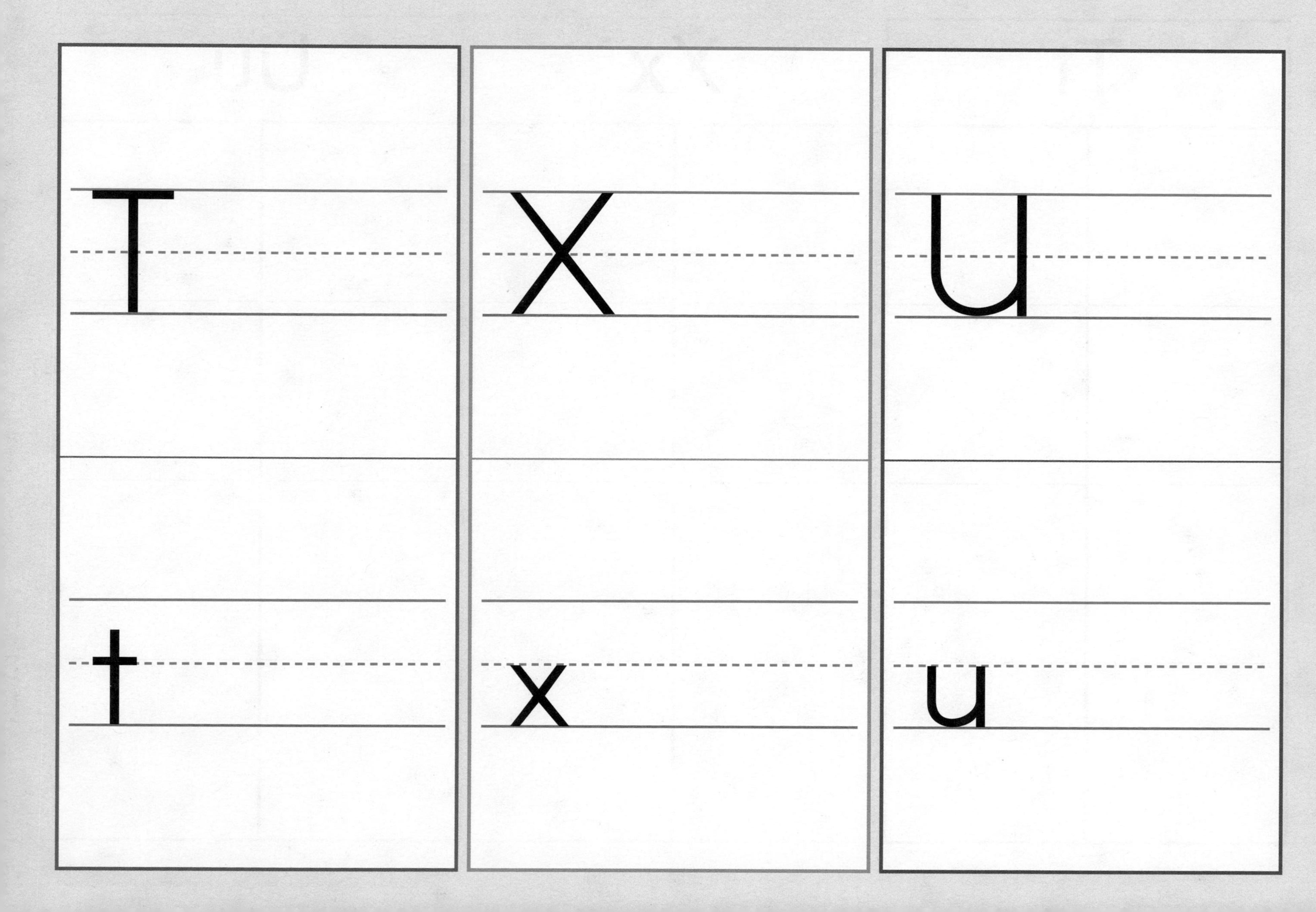
T
X
U
t
x
u

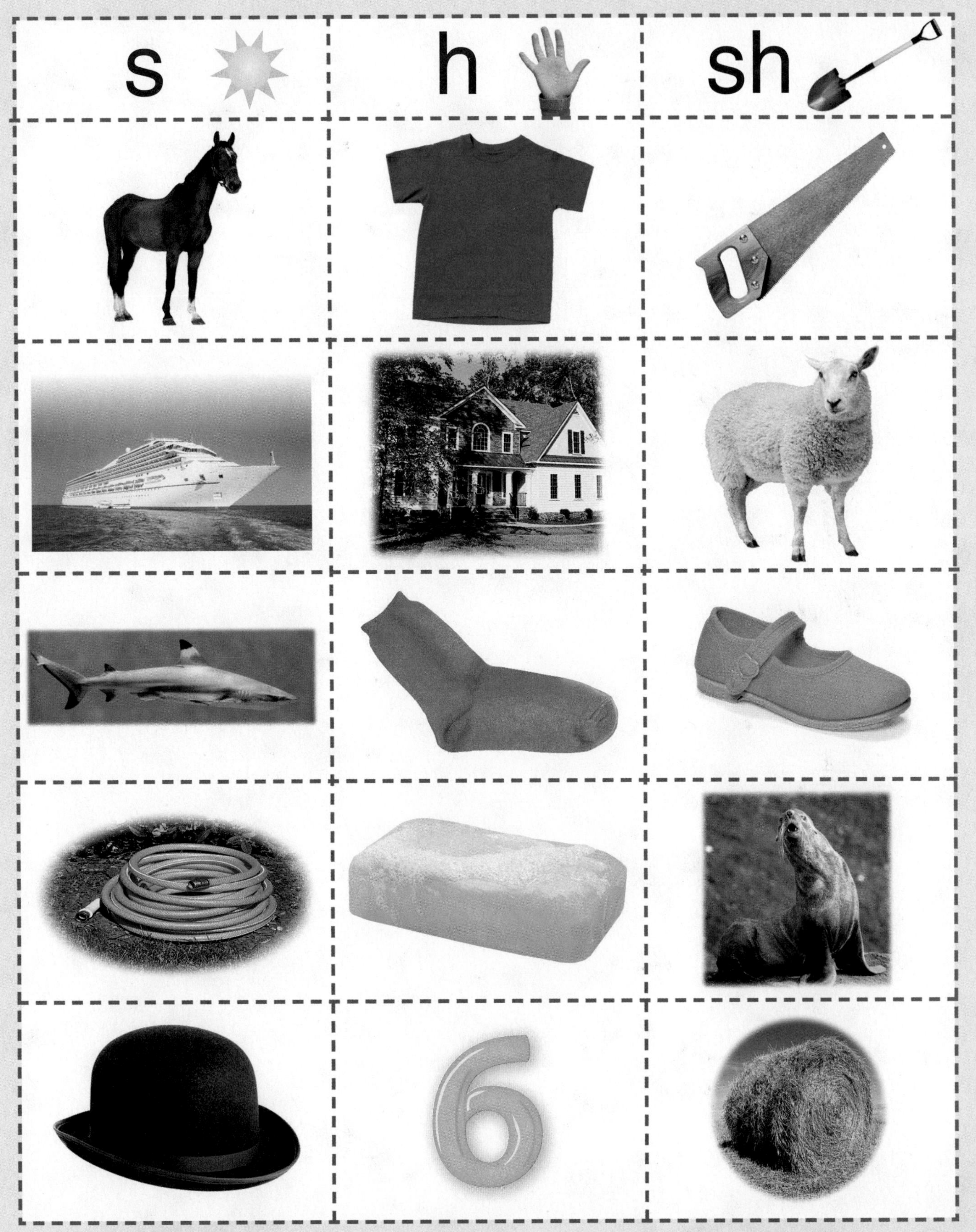
s
h
sh

s	h	sh

Draw two pictures of things that start with s, h, and sh. Write the word below each picture.

s	h	sh

Sort 39

c	h	ch

Draw two pictures of things that start with c, h, and ch. Write the word below each picture.

c	h	ch

Sort
40

h
sh
ch

h	sh	ch

Draw two pictures of things that start with h, sh, and ch. Write the word below each picture.

h	sh	ch

°F °C

th	wh

Draw two pictures of things that start with th and wh. Write the word below each picture.

th	wh

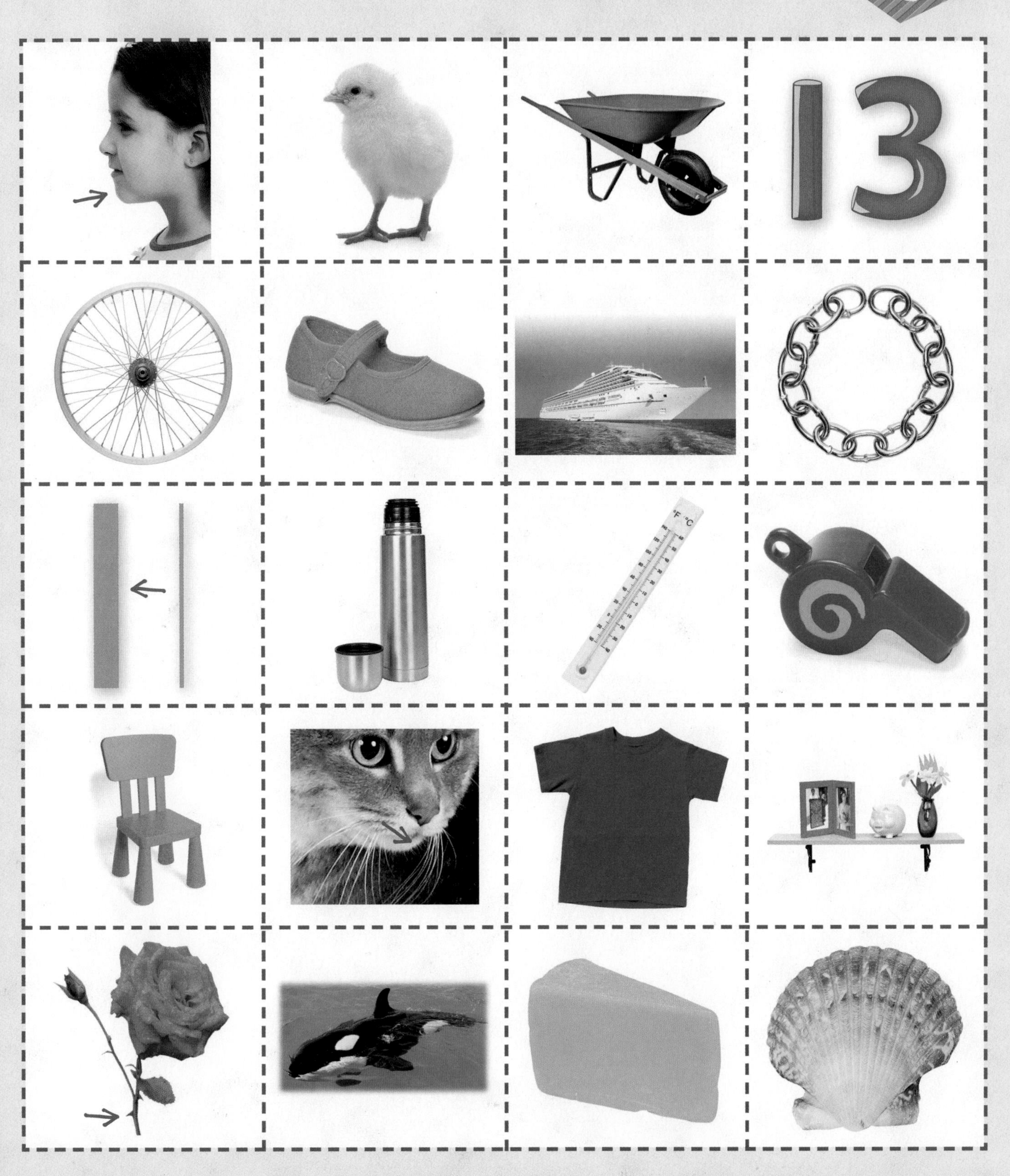
13
°F °C

sh	ch	wh	th

Draw two pictures of things that start with sh, ch, wh, and th.
Write the word below each picture.

sh	ch	wh	th

Say the name of each picture. Circle the two pictures whose names rhyme.

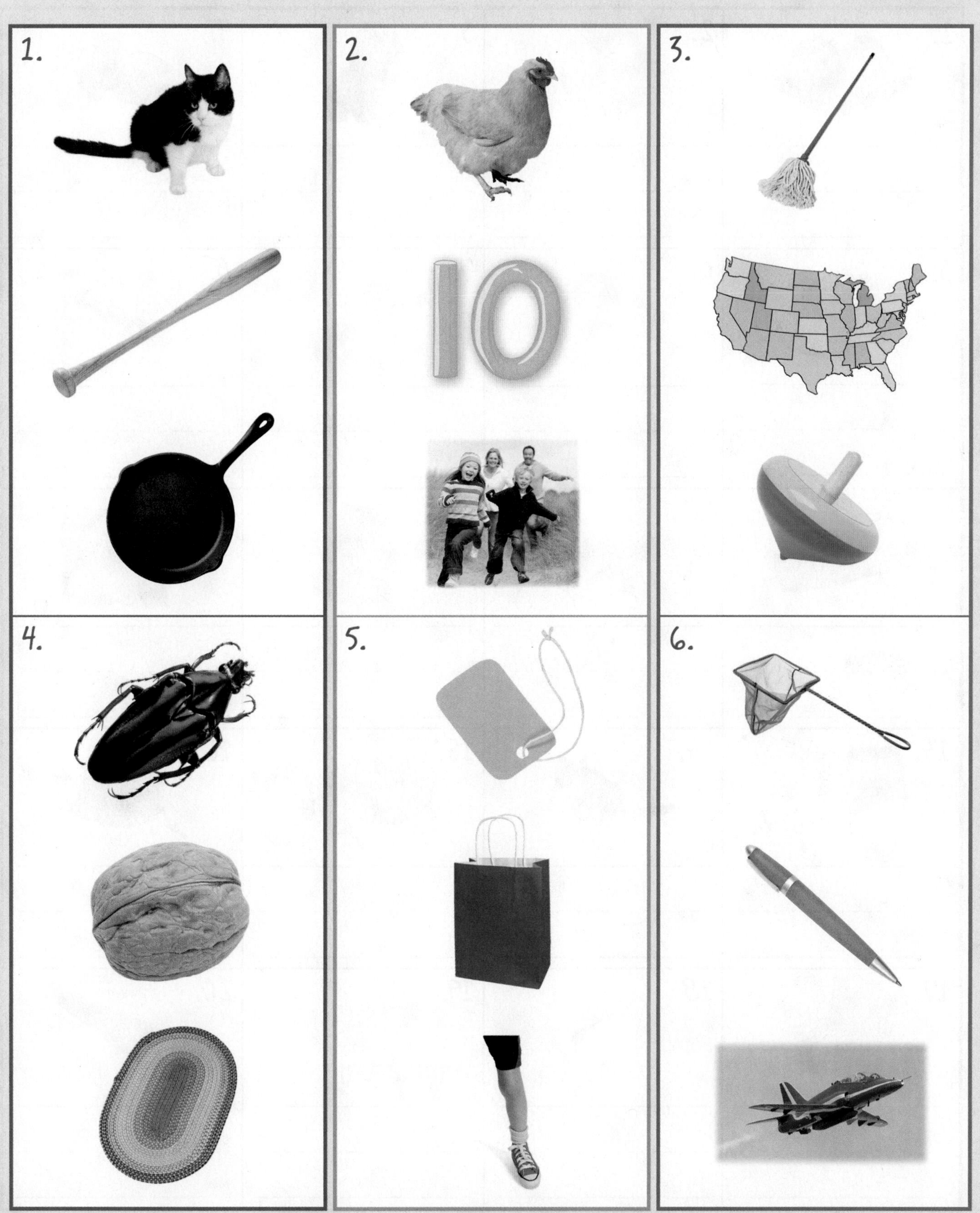

Say the name of each picture. Write the capital and lowercase letter that stands for the beginning sound.

1.	2.	3.	4.
5.	6.	7.	8.
9.	10.	11.	12.
13.	14.	15.	16.
17.	18.	19.	20.

SPELL CHECK 3

Write the matching letter next to each letter shown.

1. A ______	2. ______ e	3. B ______	4. ______ g
5. T ______	6. ______ y	7. ______ j	8. K ______
9. L ______	10. ______ m	11. ______ n	12. Q ______
13. ______ r	14. I ______	15. ______ h	16. ______ f
17. V ______	18. ______ p	19. D ______	20. X ______

Say the name of each picture. Then write its beginning digraph on the line.

1.	2.	3.	4.
5.	6.	7.	8.
9.	10.	11.	12.
13.	14.	15.	16.
17.	18.	19.	20.